UNICORN
POSTCARD BOOK

by Michael Green

Running Press
Philadelphia, Pennsylvania

Postcard Book is a trademark of Running Press Book Publishers.

Canadian representatives: General Publishing Co., Ltd.,
30 Lesmill Road, Don Mills, Ontario M3B 2T6.
International representatives: Worldwide Media Services, Inc.,
115 East Twenty-third Street, New York, New York 10010.

9   8   7   6   5

The digit on the right indicates the number of this printing.

ISBN: 0-89471-423-6 (Paper)
Cover design by Toby Schmidt.
Cover illustration by Michael Green.
Typography: by rci, Philadelphia, Pennsylvania.
Printed and bound in the United States of America by Innovation Printing.

This book can be ordered by mail from the publisher. Please add $1.50 postage
and handling for each copy. **But try your bookstore first!**

Running Press
Book Publishers
125 South Twenty-second Street
Philadelphia, Pennsylvania 19103

INTRODUCTION

The pictures reproduced on these postcards are drawn from the fabulous *Unicornis* Manuscript—an extraordinary document which, according to legend, languished for more than four centuries in the care of the Collegium Gnosticum, a mysterious Gnostic brotherhood. This curious work, a strange amalgam of Medieval and early Renaissance thought, was only recently brought to public attention through the ministrations of Michael Green, who assisted its translation and publication as *De Historia et Veritate Unicornis [On the History and Truth of the Unicorn]*.

When pressed to substantiate the manuscript's authenticity, Green invariably repeated the following story as his only explanation:

> *A good but somewhat literal-minded king had as his friend and trusted advisor a certain tentmaker who lived outside the city. One day the King found the tentmaker discoursing to several students on the power of Truth: "Seek the Truth first and last in all matters," he proclaimed. "Truth is the way and the goal of the enlightened life."*
>
> *For some reason, this struck the King most forcibly. "Aha!" he cried, "Of course!" and rode off without delay.*
>
> *Returning to his palace, the King announced that henceforth, all his subjects would be required to speak*

the truth, and anyone caught lying would be hanged. A gallows was erected in the market square and criers posted at the city gates to advise all visitors of the new law.

The next day, who should ride up on his donkey but the tentmaker. A captain and his guard dutifully stopped him at the gate. "Ho," said the captain, "Where are you going?"

"I am going," replied the tentmaker, "to be hanged."

"What?" cried the captain. "A liar indeed! Take this man away!"

"Where to?" asked the guard.

"To be hanged, of course."

"But then he shall be telling the truth," replied the guard.

So the two soldiers, who could neither hang their prisoner nor release him, brought him to the King, who learned that the Real Truth is not always found on the surface of things nor is subject to laws.

Green—a reclusive minor author and illustrator living somewhere in Pennsylvania—is unavailable for further comment. Anyone interested in more information about the *Unicornis* Manuscript is urged to review the complete version, available in libraries, bookstores, or directly from Running Press.

GAZING UNICORN

Pen and ink and watercolor on paper, 28 by 35.6 cm.
"The creature's vision is most keen, but not to be measured against that of hawks and other sharp-eyed beasts, for the Unicorn sees things not visible to any other animal."

From the book *UNICORNIS: On the History and Truth of the Unicorn*, published by Running Press. Copyright © 1983, 1986 by Michael Green. All rights reserved.

UNICORN IN TEMPEST
Brown, red, and white chalk on paper. 28.2 by 40 cm.
"The Unicorn exults in the tempest and braves the fiercest blasts, rarely seeking shelter, for these raw displays of Nature are to him a pale reminder of the swirling forces of his birth."

De hominum Unicorniumque commercio

Sanctus. Sanctus. Sanctus——
Valde antiquum hunc commercium
inter creaturas tam dissimiles——
Valde mirabilis haec locutio
sine verbis——
sermo in linguis——
oratio antecedens
omnem rationem——

UNICORN AND GIRL COMMUNING
Pen and ink, brown and white chalk on paper, 24.4 by 35.6 cm.
"Holy! Holy! Holy! Ancient indeed, this communion between creatures so unlike. Wonderful indeed, this language without tongues, this speech that will not be captured in a skein of words."

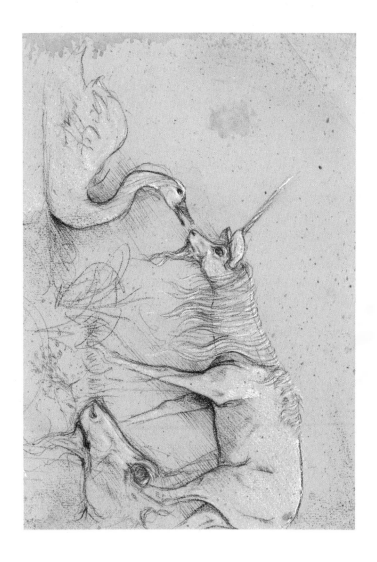

UNICORN AND SWAN

Brown and white chalk on green-grey paper, 28.2 by 44.6 cm.

"All animals love him, for among the beasts he is the most affectionate . . . His mere presence quickens in them a dim awareness of their own highest nature and divine creation."

THE CHILDREN OF THE UNICORN
Pen and ink, red and white chalk, and watercolor on paper, 28 by 35.4 cm.

"Long and delightful are their adventurous wanderings. But at the last, some of the beasts long to know the kindred race of Man that lives in that far-off, fallen realm. Then they traverse the boundaries that divide the worlds and gaze upon us in secret, loving us although they know not why."

From the book UNICORNIS: On the History and Truth of the Unicorn, published by Running Press. Copyright © 1983, 1986 by Michael Green. All rights reserved.

UNICORN AND ANCHORITE

Pen and ink and colored chalks on paper, 28 by 36.2 cm.

"All that exists here is to be found [in the realm of the Unicorn] also. But there every object seems to be the true original of its kind, and newly created, of which the examples we know are but pale reflections. What pen can trace a world without corruption? Or what brush paint colors no eyes have seen before?"

From the book UNICORNIS: *On the History and Truth of the Unicorn*, published by Running Press. Copyright © 1983, 1986 by Michael Green. All rights reserved.

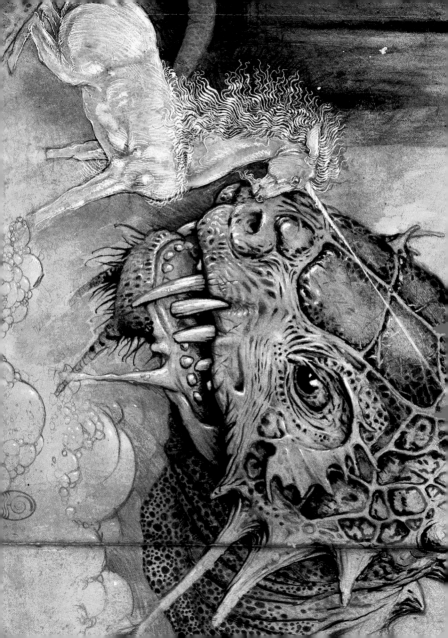

UNICORN AND DRAGON
Pen and ink, red and white chalk on paper, 49.8 by 35.6 cm.
"Now, the Unicorn oversees all dominions of this world, and so in shadows he finally must confront the Worm. No creature exceeds the Unicorn in quickness or in courage, but vast and subtle is the knowledge of the Dragon."

From the book UNICORNIS: On the History and Truth of the Unicorn, published by Running Press. Copyright © 1983, 1986 by Michael Green. All rights reserved.

STUDY OF LEAPING UNICORNS
Pen and ink and watercolor on paper, 28 by 35.6 cm.
"In the splendor of his solitude, the Unicorn is a beast transformed, expressing his rapture in great soaring leaps that are unequaled in all the animal kingdom. In them is revealed the creature's hidden nature, which is sobering to view."

From the book UNICORNS: On the History and Truth of the Unicorn, published by Running Press. Copyright © 1983, 1986 by Michael Green. All rights reserved.

STUDY OF UNICORN GAZING
Brown and white chalk on coarse grey paper, 20.2 by 22.2 cm.
"At dawn, a Unicorn will pause in his pursuits and gaze into the rising
sun—perhaps as a form of devotion."

From the book UNICORNIS: *On the History and Truth of the Unicorn,*
published by Running Press. Copyright © 1983, 1986 by Michael
Green. All rights reserved.

Multos per modos referunt se UNICORNIS ab aliis bestiis et per modum
quoque partiendi. Nunquidem dimittet caput ad cibos et terram descendendo: edit
minus homini bene nota. Nunquam aquam bibere
sumpsit ex amne uny fonte semper
queritur locum in quo catarracta

repetiturus in quo bibere
potest caput ante et
separate elevat

UNICORN DRINKING FROM WATERFALL
Pen and ink and watercolor on paper. 24.2 by 35.6 cm.

"In many ways does the Unicorn set himself apart from other animals, and also in the matter of his feeding . . . . Nor will he lap water from a spring or stream, but always seeks a waterfall and there drinks with his head held high."

UNICORN AND A PRINCESS
Oil on paper, 50.2 by 36.4 cm.
"When thou gazest into his eyes, gird thyself; for he knows all the history of our Race, and his unbroken memories reach back across the years to vast and powerful dominions now utterly undone by Fate and Time."

TITLE PAGE OF "DE HISTORIA ET VERITATE UNICORNIS"
Pen and ink and oil [?] on paper, 30.4 by 45.6 cm.

"O Reader: If thou art neither scribe nor sacrificer, cast not thy gaze upon this book, for it contains secret teachings useful only to the few and troubling to the many. And if thou seekest only mere amusement, read no further. But if thou art an earnest pilgrim on the path of Life, then open, read, and ponder."

THE RIDER OF THE UNICORN

Pen and ink, colored chalks, and wash on grey paper, 25 by 40.2 cm.

"The gentle Unicorn has also known the echoing void and so is withal a wild thing, and untamable. Then who can mount this shining beast? . . . It is said, 'Who rides the wind may ride the Unicorn.' And: 'Who calms the seas and settles the storm, only he the Unicorn will bear.'"

From the book *UNICORNIS: On the History and Truth of the Unicorn,* published by Running Press. Copyright © 1983, 1986 by Michael Green.

OF THE SEVEN HOUSES OF THE UNICORN: THE KARKADAM

Red and white chalk on paper, 28 by 35.6 cm.

"The Karkadam are the lords of loneliness and desolate lands. Nowhere do they abide for long, but wander ceaselessly, restless and untamed."

From the book *UNICORNIS: On the History and Truth of the Unicorn,* published by Running Press. Copyright © 1983, 1986 by Michael Green. All rights reserved.

SILVA·BROCILEANDENSIS·

THE FOREST OF BROCILEANDE
Oil on sized paper. 45.6 by 30.4 cm.

"This path was green with soft moss and strewn with tiny flowers. My heart was lightened by the music of running waters and the sweet calls of many birds. Then security and great peace descended upon me, for I saw that my Fate would come; I did not need to seek it out, and needed only to follow that bold and shining Horn, and not trouble myself where it should lead."

From the book *UNICORNIS. On the History and Truth of the Unicorn,* published by Running Press. Copyright © 1983, 1986 by Michael Green. All rights reserved.

Dominica in Hebr iiii Aprilis

Circa horam quartam Sylvanius, eremus noster, sedebat iuxta margin,
iuxta hortum maiorem. Non longe ego ambulans, herbas et olera legens
ad medicinam. Sylvanius vero, praecande contemplans, paene dormiens
sicut mos illi. Interim imperio aperte creaturam candida. Nulla fallacia
eorum candida. Unicornem erat. Stabat illa coram Sylvanio,
dignas aliquos passus, facile coquum intuens. Tacita, sicut eram
rorem. O Tu eram servavit eam vidi an non, non cognovi. Signum vel
motum nullum edidit. Ad eam unam signum horam mansterunt viri et
unicornis, neuter se movens omnino. Mansi immobilis, videns stupens
a velis coorekuri, similis cinnamomo. Creatura tandem verse voltavit et
paulo mihi propio vangaz. Trankuile, aspectans vultum meum. Visum domi
genae meae lacrimis madekerunt, unicornis videndas. Et

Hunc credo Sylvanium et creaturam illam conlocuros esse, charitate ingentorum
Nihil non licit dicui dicere de hoc mysterio. Experam
haevayriustei redizum—Ille siloutre hunc mihi
poterit. Ille vir peritus de omni garibile et
quibusdam aliis——————————

HERMIT AND UNICORN
Pen and ink on paper, 24.4 by 35.6 cm.
"Now Sylvanius was deep in contemplation, as is his custom, when there approached him a white creature. There could be no mistake—its single horn was white and shining: it was a Unicorn. In full view it stood, only a few paces from Sylvanius, regarding him as silently as the fall of dew."

De historia et veritate
Unicornis

INFORMAL LIFE STUDY
Pen and watercolor on paper, 24 by 35.4 cm.
"On the History and Truth of the Unicorn."

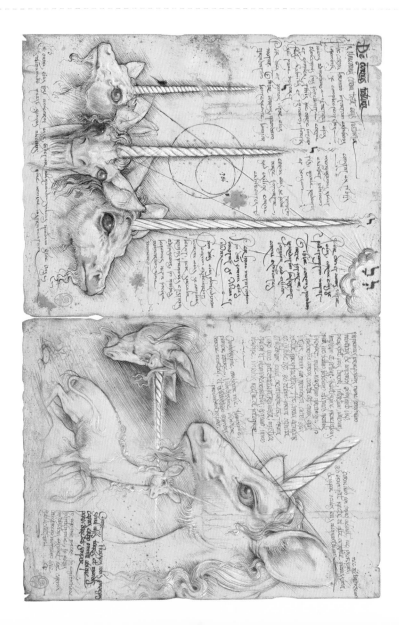

On The Nature of the Horn

Pen and ink with traces of white chalk on paper. L. 28 by 35.2 cm. R. 28 by 35.2 cm.

"Now of all aspects of the Unicorn, what holds chief sway over the mind of Man is his Horn—spiraling, solitary, great, and powerful . . . In hue it is shining white, smoother than ivory—yet vibrant with life, even more so than mortal flesh, and wedded to farthest-seeing senses. At once it occupies both this and other realms, and is thus able to penetrate all substances."

SAGE HOLDING UNICORN'S HORN
Black and white chalks on coarse grey paper, 29.2 by 44.2 cm.
"From his wooden chest, Eugnostos lifted something swaddled in damasked cloth and unwrapped it and held it in the sunlight. It was a mighty horn, set in archaic silver. Silently we gazed on it together, and the world seemed to open into a different kind of time."

From the book *UNICORNIS: On the History and Truth of the Unicorn,* published by Running Press. Copyright © 1983, 1986 by Michael Green. All rights reserved.

De UNICORNIUM Cibo

Hoc speculum bonum est valde. In terris eius progrediuntur tempore indeterminato sed eodem diversis ut omnes fructus eius maturescant in tempore suo

Nonne praeveniuntur omnes aures recentes creaturae ex hac abundantia. Mirare debetis unicornem omni modo communi sed tamen eanam est idem: alimenta videtur dicere itaque supernaturalia moenia mundi. Ex hoc videre possumus eam carni ligneam manu alias legvirae: corpus eius negari diceremur. legitimus dicere eius formam spiritualem esse, eam vero corporealem esse non minus rerum dici potest. Inter duos quidem eosdem cibos sumit quos aliae. legitur etiam, eodem studio.

Cum tamen cenam sumit UNICORNIS, vult se non esse furens idcirco

de terrae fructus tantum qui illi sponte offert Natura abundans

Cum illis carent, eam dici semper pasci folia arborum generosum.

Sitis eius satiatur aquis tantum rivi.

Tibi de nostra videntur fructus sumit Unicornis in eo ramo pendens postea fructus magni maioresque uberiores.

Inter unicornum et virginem nexus quidam non inter
homines nexus
et unicornem viri mirantur cum reverentia
vel cum timore vel cum cupiditate spiritus.   De virginibus

Sed ex virgine elicit
unicornis, mirae ac
indignem virgam
puellae, cui adligatur
unicornis sicut flosculo
fragranti apes
Et in hac communione
mysterium dulce

THE MAIDEN AND THE UNICORN
Brown, blue, and white chalk on paper, 28 by 35.6 cm.

"Between the Unicorn and maidens lies a secret bond not known by men. For … women have not the thirst for dominion over others by which men are constantly possessed. Those who crave dominion seldom suffer themselves to be led … Know yourselves, brethren: Are ye as wise as ye flatter yourselves to be? He who wishes to lead, let him learn to follow."

UNICORN AND CHILD
Pen and ink with white chalk on grey paper. 32.2 by 29.8 cm.
"And children with the Unicorn seem to enjoy a remarkable familiarity."

From the book UNICORNS. *On the History and Truth of the Unicorn,* published by Running Press. Copyright © 1983, 1986 by Michael Green.

THE UNICORN IN HIS BATTLE RAPTURE

Brown, red, and white chalk on paper, 28.2 by 36.6 cm.

"In battle he falls upon his foes like a bright spear of flame. His merciless pointed hooves are swift and accurate. But his Horn is an instrument of healing and of knowledge, and never will he employ it in mortal combat, lest it be fouled with blood."

UNICORN AND DREAMING MAIDEN IN LANDSCAPE

Oil on treated paper, 31.8 by 49.2 cm.

"The Unicorn has a singular virtue: that he can penetrate our dreams, and there address us. Therefore take heed, O Dreamer, when the Unicorn appears to thee. Though his speech is unlike any tongue of Man, yet shalt thou comprehend!"

From the book *UNICORNS: On the History and Truth of the Unicorn*, published by Running Press. Copyright © 1983, 1986 by Michael Green. All rights reserved.

OF THE SEVEN HOUSES OF THE UNICORN: THE KILLINA

Pen and ink, red and white chalk on paper, 28.2 by 35.6 cm.

"In this world, their ministry is to the Kingdoms of the East, but seldom need they intrude themselves upon the affairs of Man. Thus their appearance is an omen of portentous import, heralding the reign of a great king, or a high and noble birth."

From the book *UNICORNIS: On the History and Truth of the Unicorn,* published by Running Press. Copyright © 1983, 1986 by Michael Green. All rights reserved.

THE COUNCIL OF UNICORNS

Oil glazes on paper, 45.6 by 30 cm.

"When some great need comes to pass, the more ancient of the Unicorns gather, unbidden and of their own accord, in some remote place, whether lofty crag or secret glade. And there they hold their council. Abandoning the use of tongues . . . from mind to mind they gaze, thinking back over all the ages gone by, even to the very roots of Time when the Earth was new."

From the book *UNICORNIS: On the History and Truth of the Unicorn,* published by Running Press. Copyright © 1983, 1986 by Michael Green. All rights reserved.